SELECTED FROM

DARK THEY WERE, AND GOLDEN-EYED

Ray Bradbury

Supplementary material by George Ochoa and
the staff of Literacy Volunteers of New York City

WRITERS' VOICES
Literacy Volunteers of New York City

WRITERS' VOICES™ was made possible by grants from: An anonymous foundation; The Vincent Astor Foundation; Booth Ferris Foundation; Exxon Corporation; James Money Management, Inc.; Knight Foundation; Philip Morris Companies Inc.; Scripps Howard Foundation; The House of Seagram and H.W. Wilson Foundation.

ATTENTION READERS: We would like to hear what you think about our books. Please send your comments or suggestions to:

> The Editors
> Literacy Volunteers of New York City
> 121 Avenue of the Americas
> New York, NY 10013

Selection: From DARK THEY WERE, AND GOLDEN-EYED by Ray Bradbury. Copyright © 1949, renewed 1977 by Ray Bradbury. Reprinted by permission of Don Congdon Associates, Inc.

Supplementary materials © 1991 by Literacy Volunteers of New York City Inc.

Printed in the United States of America.

97 96 95 94 93 92 91 10 9 8 7 6 5 4 3 2 1

First LVNYC Printing: March 1991

ISBN 0-929631-24-2

Writers' Voices is a series of books published by Literacy Volunteers of New York City Inc., 121 Avenue of the Americas, New York, NY 10013. The words, "Writers' Voices," are a trademark of Literacy Volunteers of New York City.

Cover designed by Paul Davis Studio; interior designed by Paolo Pepe.

Executive Director, LVNYC: Eli Zal
Publishing Director, LVNYC: Nancy McCord
Managing Editor: Sarah Kirshner
Publishing Coordinator: Yvette Martinez-Gonzalez

LVNYC is an affiliate of Literacy Volunteers of America.

ACKNOWLEDGMENTS

Literacy Volunteers of New York City gratefully acknowledges the generous support of the following foundations and corporations that made the publication of WRITERS' VOICES and NEW WRITERS' VOICES possible: An anonymous foundation; The Vincent Astor Foundation; Booth Ferris Foundation; Exxon Corporation; James Money Management, Inc.; Knight Foundation; Philip Morris Companies Inc.; Scripps Howard Foundation; The House of Seagram and H.W. Wilson Foundation.

This book could not have been realized without the kind and generous cooperation of the author, Ray Bradbury, and his agent, Don Congdon Associates, Inc.

We deeply appreciate the contributions of the following suppliers: Cam Steel Die Rule Works Inc. (steel cutting die for display); Canadian Pacific Forest Products Ltd. (text stock); ComCom (text typesetting); Horizon Paper Co., Inc. and Domtar Fine Papers (cover stock); MCUSA (display header); Delta Corrugated Container (corrugated display); Phototype Color Graphics (cover color separations); and Arcata Graphics Company/Buffalo (cover and text printing and binding).

For their guidance, support and hard work, we are indebted to the LVNYC Board of Directors' Publishing Committee: James E. Galton, Marvel Entertainment Group; Virginia Barber, Virginia Barber Literary Agency, Inc.; Doris Bass, Bantam Doubleday Dell; Jeff Brown; Jerry Butler, William Morrow & Company, Inc.; George P. Davidson, Ballantine Books; Joy M. Gannon, St. Martin's Press; Walter Kiechel, *Fortune*; Geraldine

E. Rhoads, Diamandis Communications Inc.; Virginia Rice, Reader's Digest; Martin Singerman, News America Publishing, Inc.; James L. Stanko, James Money Management, Inc. and F. Robert Stein, Pryor, Cashman, Sherman & Flynn.

Thanks also to George Davidson, Caron Harris, Yayun Chang, Steve Palmer and Melissa Sann of Ballantine Books for producing this book; Virginia Barber for assistance in obtaining permissions; George Ochoa for his skill and diligence in the research and writing of the supplementary material for this book; Natalie Bowen for her thoughtful copyediting and suggestions; Helen Morris for her dedication and helpful contributions at so many stages of the book; and to Marcia Friedman for proofreading.

Our thanks to Paul Davis Studio and Myrna Davis, Paul Davis, Jeanine Esposito, Alex Ginns and Frank Begrowicz for their inspired design of the covers of these books. Thanks also to Paolo Pepe for his sensitive design of the interior of this book, Karen Bernath for design of maps and diagrams, and Ron Bel Bruno for his timely help.

And finally, special credit must be given to Marilyn Boutwell, Jean Fargo and Gary Murphy of the LVNYC staff for their contributions to the educational and editorial content of these books.

CONTENTS

Note to the Reader

Dark They Were, and Golden-Eyed is a science fiction short story. In science fiction, the author asks the reader to journey into the unknown. Readers must consider new possibilities. Some things in the story may be strange and alien. Yet other parts of the story may touch on something we recognize in ourselves.

Every writer has a special voice. That is why we call our series *Writers' Voices*. We chose *Dark They Were, and Golden-Eyed* because the special voice of a science fiction writer, Ray Bradbury, can be clearly heard. It comes from a book of his science fiction short stories called *S Is for Space*.

• Reading "About the Selection *Dark They Were, and Golden-Eyed*" on page 10 will help you begin thinking about what you will find in the story.

In addition to *Dark They Were, and Golden-Eyed*, this book includes chapters with interesting and helpful information related to the story. You may read these before or after reading the story. You may choose to read some or all of these chapters.

• If you would like to know more about what is different about reading and writing science fiction, read the chapter "About Science Fiction and Fantasy" on page 51.

• If you would like more information about outer space, look at the chapters called "About Mars" on page 55 and "About Space Travel" on page 60.

• Many readers enjoy finding out about the person who wrote the story. Sometimes this information will give you more insight into the story. You can find out more about Ray Bradbury in the chapter on page 49.

If you are a new reader, you may want to have this book read aloud to you, perhaps more than once. Even if you are a more experienced reader, you may enjoy hearing it read aloud before reading it silently to yourself.

We encourage you to read *actively*. Here are some things you can do:

BEFORE READING

• Read the front and back covers of the

book, and look at the cover illustration. Ask yourself what you expect the story to be about.

• Think about why you want to read this book. Perhaps you enjoy reading science fiction.

• Look at the Contents page. See where you can find a map of the solar system and other information. Decide what you want to read and in what order.

DURING READING

• There may be made-up Martian words and names or other words that are difficult to read. Keep reading to see if the meaning becomes clear. If it doesn't, go back and re-read the difficult part or discuss it with others. Or look in the glossary on page 41 to see if you can find the word. Or look up the word in a dictionary.

• Ask yourself questions as you read. For example: How are the people from Earth changing on Mars?

• Think about what you have read. Did you identify with Harry or Cora? Did the story change your thinking about what it would be like to live on another planet?
• Talk with others about your thoughts.
• Try some of the questions and activities in "Questions for the Reader" on page 44. They are meant to help you discover more about what you have read and how it relates to you.

The editors of *Writers' Voices* hope you will write to us. We want to know your thoughts about our books.

About the Selection *Dark They Were, and Golden-Eyed*

Ray Bradbury's short story *Dark They Were, and Golden-Eyed* was written in 1949 and is set in the future, in a time when space travel is common. It is the story of a man from Earth who moves with his family to the planet Mars. From the start, he fears that something terrible will happen. It turns out he is right.

The man's name is Harry Bittering. His wife is Cora, and their three children are Dan, Laura and David. They travel to Mars by rocket. There they join other people from the United States who have already built a town.

The Earth people do not find any Martians. But they do find cities that the Martians built a long time ago. The cities are empty now. Yet Bittering fears that Earth people do not belong on Mars. He wonders if he should go back to Earth.

Then they hear on the radio about an atomic war on Earth. Atom bombs have destroyed much of the United States. The Bittering family cannot go back.

Soon, odd changes start to happen. Food begins to taste different. Red roses turn green. The Earth people's skin becomes darker, and their eyes golden. They begin to look the way the Martians used to look.

Bittering is afraid he will lose his human identity if he does not leave Mars. But it may already be too late.

The author, Ray Bradbury, has set many stories on Mars. In *Dark They Were, and Golden-Eyed,* he makes up Martian words that sound foreign and strange. He creates the Martian words *Iorrt* for *Earth, Utha* for *father,* and *Linnl* for a boy's name.

The settlers from Earth use names they know for places on Mars. These names include those of American presidents and famous businessmen. They also include the Indian names that were given to American towns and states.

Bradbury adds special details to remind you that you are on another world. One is the "voice-clock" that the Bitterings have. This is a clock that sings the time instead of just showing it. At another point, Bittering looks up at a green star. It is the planet Earth he is looking at.

In this story, the people from Earth gradually lose their human identity. It almost seems as if the Martian winds and rivers are wearing the people away, in the way winds and rivers on Earth wear stone away.

Perhaps this story will remind you of a time you were afraid of the unknown. Perhaps it will make you think about how people change over time, almost without knowing it.

DARK THEY WERE,
AND
GOLDEN-EYED

RAY BRADBURY

The rocket metal cooled in the meadow winds. Its lid gave a bulging *pop*. From its clock interior stepped a man, a woman, and three children. The other passengers whispered away across the Martian meadow, leaving the man alone among his family.

The man felt his hair flutter and the tissues of his body draw tight as if he were standing at the center of a vacuum. His wife, before him, seemed almost to whirl away in smoke. The children, small seeds, might at any instant be sown to all the Martian climes.

The children looked up at him, as people look to the sun to tell what time of their life it is. His face was cold.

"What's wrong?" asked his wife.

"Let's get back on the rocket."

"Go back to Earth?"

"Yes! Listen!"

The wind blew as if to flake away their identities. At any moment the Martian air might draw his soul from him, as marrow comes from a white bone. He felt submerged in a chemical that could dissolve his intellect and burn away his past.

They looked at Martian hills that time had worn with a crushing pressure of years. They saw the old cities, lost in their meadows, lying like children's delicate bones among the blowing lakes of grass.

"Chin up, Harry," said his wife. "It's too late. We've come over sixty million miles."

The children with their yellow hair hollered at the deep dome of Martian sky. There was no answer but the racing hiss of wind through the stiff grass.

He picked up the luggage in his cold hands. "Here we go," he said—a man standing on the edge of a sea, ready to wade in and be drowned.

They walked into town.

Their name was Bittering. Harry and his wife Cora; Dan, Laura, and David. They built a small white cottage and ate good breakfasts there, but the fear was never gone. It lay with Mr. Bittering and Mrs. Bittering, a third unbidden partner at every midnight talk, at every dawn awakening.

"I feel like a salt crystal," he said, "in a mountain stream, being washed away. We don't belong here. We're Earth people. This is Mars. It was meant for Martians. For heaven's sake, Cora, let's buy tickets for home!"

But she only shook her head. "One day the atom bomb will fix Earth. Then we'll be safe here."

"Safe and insane!"

Tick-tock, seven o'clock sang the voice-clock; *time to get up.* And they did.

Something made him check everything each morning—warm hearth, potted blood-geraniums—precisely as if he expected something to be amiss. The morning paper was toast-warm from the 6 A.M. Earth rocket. He broke its seal and tilted it at his breakfast place. He forced himself to be convivial.

"Colonial days all over again," he declared. "Why, in ten years there'll be a million Earthmen on Mars. Big cities, everything! They said we'd fail. Said the Martians would resent our invasion. But did we find any Martians? Not a living soul! Oh, we found their empty cities, but no one in them. Right?"

A river of wind submerged the house. When the windows ceased rattling Mr. Bittering swallowed and looked at the children.

"I don't know," said David. "Maybe there're Martians around we don't see. Sometimes nights I think I hear 'em. I hear the wind. The sand hits my window. I get scared. And I see those towns way up in the mountains where the Martians lived a long time ago. And I think I see things moving around those towns, Papa. And I wonder if those Martians *mind* us living here. I wonder if they won't do something to us for coming here."

"Nonsense!" Mr. Bittering looked out the windows. "We're clean, decent people." He looked at his children. "All dead cities have some kind of ghosts in them. Memories, I mean." He stared at the hills. "You see a staircase and you wonder what Martians looked like climbing it. You see Martian paintings and you wonder what the painter was like. You make a little ghost in your mind, a memory. It's quite natural. Imagination." He stopped.

"You haven't been prowling up in those ruins, have you?"

"No, Papa." David looked at his shoes.

"See that you stay away from them. Pass the jam."

"Just the same," said little David, "I bet something happens."

Something happened that afternoon.

Laura stumbled through the settlement, crying. She dashed blindly onto the porch.

"Mother, Father—the war, Earth!" she sobbed. "A radio flash just came. Atom bombs hit New York! All the space rockets blown up. No more rockets to Mars, ever!"

"Oh, Harry!" The mother held on to her husband and daughter.

"Are you sure, Laura?" asked the father quietly.

Laura wept. "We're stranded on Mars, forever and ever!"

For a long time there was only the sound of the wind in the late afternoon.

Alone, thought Bittering. Only a thousand of us here. No way back. No way. No way. Sweat poured from his face and his hands and his body; he was drenched in the hotness of his fear. He wanted to strike Laura, cry, "No, you're lying! The rockets will come back!" Instead, he stroked Laura's head against him and said, "The rockets will get through someday."

"Father, what will we do?"

"Go about our business, of course. Raise crops and children. Wait. Keep things going until the war ends and the rockets come again."

The two boys stepped out onto the porch.

"Children," he said, sitting there, looking beyond them, "I've something to tell you."

"We know," they said.

In the following days, Bittering wandered often through the garden to stand alone in his fear. As long as the rockets had spun a silver web across space, he had been able to accept Mars. For he had always told himself: Tomorrow, if I want, I can buy a ticket and go back to Earth.

But now: The web gone, the rockets lying in jigsaw heaps of molten girder and unsnaked wire. Earth people left to the strangeness of Mars, the cinnamon dusts and wine airs, to be baked like gingerbread shapes in Martian summers, put into harvested storage by Martian winters. What would happen to him, the others? This was the moment Mars had waited for. Now it would eat them.

He got down on his knees in the flower bed, a spade in his nervous hands. Work, he thought, work and forget.

He glanced up from the garden to the Martian mountains. He thought of the proud old Martian names that had once been on those peaks. Earthmen, dropping from the sky, had gazed upon hills, rivers, Martian seats left nameless in spite of names. Once Martians had built cities, named cities; climbed mountains, named mountains; sailed seas, named seas. Mountains melted, seas drained, cities tumbled. In spite of this, the Earthmen had felt a silent guilt at putting new names to these ancient hills and valleys.

Nevertheless, man lives by symbol and label. The names were given.

Mr. Bittering felt very alone in his garden under the Martian sun, anachronism bent here, planting Earth flowers in a wild soil.

Think. Keep thinking. Different things. Keep your mind free of Earth, the atom war, the lost rockets.

He perspired. He glanced about. No one

watching. He removed his tie. Pretty bold, he
thought. First your coat off, now your tie. He
hung it neatly on a peach tree he had imported
as a sapling from Massachusetts.

He returned to his philosophy of names and
mountains. The Earthmen had changed names.
Now there were Hormel Valleys, Roosevelt
Seas, Ford Hills, Vanderbilt Plateaus, Rockefeller Rivers, on Mars. It wasn't right. The
American settlers had shown wisdom, using
old Indian prairie names: Wisconsin, Minnesota, Idaho, Ohio, Utah, Milwaukee, Waukegan, Osseo. The old names, the old meanings.

Staring at the mountains wildly, he thought:
Are you up there? All the dead ones, you Martians? Well, here we are, alone, cut off! Come
down, move us out! We're helpless!

The wind blew a shower of peach blossoms.

He put out his sun-browned hand and gave
a small cry. He touched the blossoms and
picked them up. He turned them, he touched
them again and again. Then he shouted for his
wife.

"Cora!"

She appeared at a window. He ran to her.

"Cora, these blossoms!"

She handled them.

"Do you see? They're different. They've changed! They're not peach blossoms any more!"

"Look all right to me," she said.

"They're not. They're wrong! I can't tell how. An extra petal, a leaf, something, the color, the smell!"

The children ran out in time to see their father hurrying about the garden, pulling up radishes, onions, and carrots from their beds.

"Cora, come look!"

They handled the onions, the radishes, the carrots among them.

"Do they look like carrots?"

"Yes . . . no." She hesitated. "I don't know."

"They're changed."

"Perhaps."

"You know they have! Onions but not onions, carrots but not carrots. Taste: the same but different. Smell: not like it used to be." He felt his heart pounding, and he was afraid. He dug his fingers into the earth. "Cora, what's happening? What is it? We've got to get away from this." He ran across the garden. Each tree felt his touch. "The roses. The roses. They're turning green!"

And they stood looking at the green roses.

And two days later Dan came running. "Come see the cow. I was milking her and I saw it. Come on!"

They stood in the shed and looked at their one cow.

It was growing a third horn.

And the lawn in front of their house very quietly and slowly was coloring itself like spring violets. Seed from Earth but growing up a soft purple.

"We must get away," said Bittering. "We'll eat this stuff and then we'll change—who knows to what? I can't let it happen. There's only one thing to do. Burn this food!"

"It's not poisoned."

"But it is. Subtly, very subtly. A little bit. A very little bit. We mustn't touch it."

He looked with dismay at their house. "Even the house. The wind's done something to it. The air's burned it. The fog at night. The boards, all warped out of shape. It's not an Earthman's house any more."

"Oh, your imagination!"

He put on his coat and tie. "I'm going into town. We've got to do something now. I'll be back."

"Wait, Harry!" his wife cried.

But he was gone.

In town, on the shadowy step of the grocery store, the men sat with their hands on their knees, conversing with great leisure and ease.

Mr. Bittering wanted to fire a pistol in the air.

What are you doing, you fools! he thought. Sitting here! You've heard the news—we're stranded on this planet. Well, move! Aren't you frightened? Aren't you afraid? What are you going to do?

"Hello, Harry," said everyone.

"Look," he said to them. "You did hear the news, the other day, didn't you?"

They nodded and laughed. "Sure. Sure, Harry."

"What are you going to do about it?"

"Do, Harry, do? What *can* we do?"

"Build a rocket, that's what!"

"A rocket, Harry? To go back to all that trouble? Oh, Harry!"

"But you *must* want to go back. Have you noticed the peach blossoms, the onions, the grass?"

"Why, yes, Harry, seems we did," said one of the men.

"Doesn't it scare you?"

"Can't recall that it did much, Harry."

"Idiots!"

"Now, Harry."

Bittering wanted to cry. "You've got to work with me. If we stay here, we'll all change. The air. Don't you smell it? Something in the air. A Martian virus, maybe; some seed, or a pollen. Listen to me!"

They stared at him.

"Sam," he said to one of them.

"Yes, Harry?"

"Will you help me build a rocket?"

"Harry, I got a whole load of metal and some blueprints. You want to work in my metal shop on a rocket, you're welcome. I'll sell you that metal for five hundred dollars. You should be able to construct a right pretty rocket, if you work alone, in about thirty years."

Everyone laughed.

"Don't laugh."

Sam looked at him with quiet good humor.

"Sam," Bittering said. "Your eyes—"

"What about them, Harry?"

"Didn't they used to be gray?"

"Well now, I don't remember."

"They were, weren't they?"

"Why do you ask, Harry?"

"Because now they're kind of yellow-colored."

"Is that so, Harry?" Sam said, casually.

"And you're taller and thinner—"

"You might be right, Harry."

"Sam, you shouldn't have yellow eyes."

"Harry, what color eyes have *you* got?" Sam said.

"My eyes? They're blue, of course."

"Here you are, Harry." Sam handed him a pocket mirror. "Take a look at yourself."

Mr. Bittering hesitated, and then raised the mirror to his face.

There were little, very dim flecks of new gold captured in the blue of his eyes.

"Now look what you've done," said Sam a moment later. "You've broken my mirror."

Harry Bittering moved into the metal shop and began to build the rocket. Men stood in the open door and talked and joked without raising their voices. Once in a while they gave him a hand on lifting something. But mostly they just idled and watched him with their yellowing eyes.

"It's suppertime, Harry," they said.

His wife appeared with his supper in a wicker basket.

"I won't touch it," he said. "I'll eat only food from our Deepfreeze. Food that came from Earth. Nothing from our garden."

His wife stood watching him. "You can't build a rocket."

"I worked in a shop once, when I was twenty. I know metal. Once I get it started, the others will help," he said, not looking at her, laying out the blueprints.

"Harry, Harry," she said, helplessly.

"We've got to get away, Cora. We've *got* to!"

The nights were full of wind that blew down the empty moonlit sea meadows past the little white chess cities lying for their twelve-thousandth year in the shallows. In the Earthmen's settlement, the Bittering house shook with a feeling of change.

Lying abed, Mr. Bittering felt his bones shifted, shaped, melted like gold. His wife, lying beside him, was dark from many sunny afternoons. Dark she was, and golden-eyed, burnt almost black by the sun, sleeping, and the children metallic in their beds, and the wind roaring forlorn and changing through the old peach trees, the violet grass, shaking out green rose petals.

The fear would not be stopped. It had his throat and heart. It dripped in a wetness of the arm and the temple and the trembling palm.

A green star rose in the east.

A strange word emerged from Mr. Bittering's lips.

"Iorrt. Iorrt." He repeated it.

It was a Martian word. He knew no Martian.

In the middle of the night he arose and dialed a call through to Simpson, the archaeologist.

"Simpson, what does the word *Iorrt* mean?"

"Why that's the old Martian word for our planet Earth. Why?"

"No special reason."

The telephone slipped from his hand.

"Hello, hello, hello, hello," it kept saying while he sat gazing out at the green star. "Bittering? Harry, are you there?"

The days were full of metal sound. He laid

the frame of the rocket with the reluctant help of three indifferent men. He grew very tired in an hour or so and had to sit down.

"The altitude," laughed a man.

"Are you *eating*, Harry?" asked another.

"I'm eating," he said, angrily.

"From your Deepfreeze?"

"Yes!"

"You're getting thinner, Harry."

"I'm not!"

"And taller."

"Liar!"

His wife took him aside a few days later. "Harry, I've used up all the food in the Deepfreeze. There's nothing left. I'll have to make sandwiches using food grown on Mars."

He sat down heavily.

"You must eat," she said. "You're weak."

"Yes," he said.

He took a sandwich, opened it, looked at it, and began to nibble at it.

"And take the rest of the day off," she said. "It's hot. The children want to swim in the canals and hike. Please come along."

"I can't waste time. This is a crisis!"

"Just for an hour," she urged. "A swim'll do you good."

He rose, sweating. "All right, all right. Leave me alone. I'll come."

"Good for you, Harry."

The sun was hot, the day quiet. There was only an immense staring burn upon the land. They moved along the canal, the father, the mother, the racing children in their swimsuits. They stopped and ate meat sandwiches. He saw their skin baking brown. And he saw the yellow eyes of his wife and his children, their eyes that were never yellow before. A few tremblings shook him, but were carried off in waves of pleasant heat as he lay in the sun. He was too tired to be afraid.

"Cora, how long have your eyes been yellow?"

She was bewildered. "Always, I guess."

"They didn't change from brown in the last three months?"

She bit her lips. "No. Why do you ask?"

"Never mind."

They sat there.

"The children's eyes," he said. "They're yellow, too."

"Sometimes growing children's eyes change color."

"Maybe *we're* children, too. At least to Mars. That's a thought." He laughed. "Think I'll swim."

They leaped into the canal water, and he let himself sink down and down to the bottom like a golden statue and lie there in green silence. All was water-quiet and deep, all was peace. He felt the steady, slow current drift him easily.

If I lie here long enough, he thought, the water will work and eat away my flesh until the bones show like coral. Just my skeleton left. And then the water can build on that skeleton—green things, deep water things, red things, yellow things. Change. Change. Slow, deep, silent change. And isn't that what it is up *there?*

He saw the sky submerged above him, the sun made Martian by atmosphere and time and space.

Up there, a big river, he thought, a Martian river, all of us lying deep in it, in our pebble houses, in our sunken boulder houses, like crayfish hidden, and the water washing away

our old bodies and lengthening the bones
and—

He let himself drift up through the soft light.

Dan sat on the edge of the canal, regarding
his father seriously.

"Utha," he said.

"What?" asked his father.

The boy smiled. "You know. *Utha's* the
Martian word for 'father.' "

"Where did you learn it?"

"I don't know. Around. *Utha!"*

"What do you want?"

The boy hesitated. "I—I want to change my
name."

"Change it?"

"Yes."

His mother swam over. "What's wrong with
Dan for a name?"

Dan fidgeted. "The other day you called
Dan, Dan, Dan. I didn't even hear. I said to my-
self, That's not my name. I've a new name I
want to use."

Mr. Bittering held to the side of the canal,
his body cold and his heart pounding slowly.
"What is this new name?"

"Linnl. Isn't that a good name? Can I use
it? Can't I, please?"

Mr. Bittering put his hand to his head. He thought of the silly rocket, himself working alone, himself alone even among his family, so alone.

He heard his wife say, "Why not?"

He heard himself say, "Yes, you can use it."

"Yaaa!" screamed the boy. "I'm Linnl, Linnl!"

Racing down the meadowlands, he danced and shouted.

Mr. Bittering looked at his wife. "Why did we do that?"

"I don't know," she said. "It just seemed like a good idea."

They walked into the hills. They strolled on old mosaic paths, beside still pumping fountains. The paths were covered with a thin film of cool water all summer long. You kept your bare feet cool all the day, splashing as in a creek, wading.

They came to a small deserted Martian villa with a good view of the valley. It was on top of a hill. Blue marble halls, large murals, a swimming pool. It was refreshing in this hot summertime. The Martians hadn't believed in large cities.

"How nice," said Mrs. Bittering, "if we

could move up here to this villa for the summer."

"Come on," he said. "We're going back to town. There's work to be done on the rocket."

But as he worked that night, the thought of the cool blue marble villa entered his mind. As the hours passed, the rocket seemed less important.

In the flow of days and weeks, the rocket receded and dwindled. The old fever was gone. It frightened him to think he had let it slip this way. But somehow the heat, the air, the working conditions—

He heard the men murmuring on the porch of his metal shop.

"Everyone's going. You heard?"

"All going. That's right."

Bittering came out. "Going where?" He saw a couple of trucks, loaded with children and furniture, drive down the dusty street.

"Up to the villas," said the man.

"Yeah, Harry. I'm going. So is Sam. Aren't you Sam?"

"That's right, Harry. What about you?"

"I've got work to do here."

"Work! You can finish that rocket in the autumn, when it's cooler."

He took a breath. "I got the frame all set up."

"In the autumn is better." Their voices were lazy in the heat.

"Got to work," he said.

"Autumn," they reasoned. And they sounded so sensible, so right.

"Autumn would be best," he thought. "Plenty of time, then."

No! cried part of himself, deep down, put away, locked tight, suffocating. No! No!

"In the autumn," he said.

"Come on, Harry," they all said.

"Yes," he said, feeling his flesh melt in the hot liquid air. "Yes, in the autumn. I'll begin work again then."

"I got a villa near the Tirra Canal," said someone.

"You mean the Roosevelt Canal, don't you?"

"Tirra. The old Martian name."

"But on the map—"

"Forget the map. It's Tirra now. Now I found a place in the Pillan Mountains—"

"You mean the Rockefeller Range," said Bittering.

"I mean the Pillan Mountains," said Sam.

"Yes," said Bittering, buried in the hot, swarming air. "The Pillan Mountains."

Everyone worked at loading the truck in the hot, still afternoon of the next day.

Laura, Dan, and David carried packages. Or, as they preferred to be known, Ttil, Linnl, and Werr carried packages.

The furniture was abandoned in the little white cottage.

"It looked just fine in Boston," said the mother. "And here in the cottage. But up at the villa? No. We'll get it when we come back in the autumn."

Bittering himself was quiet.

"I've some ideas on furniture for the villa," he said after a time. "Big, lazy furniture."

"What about your encyclopedia? You're taking it along, surely?"

Mr. Bittering glanced away. "I'll come and get it next week."

They turned to their daughter. "What about your New York dresses?"

The bewildered girl stared. "Why, I don't want them any more."

They shut off the gas, the water, they locked the doors and walked away. Father peered into the truck.

"Gosh, we're not taking much," he said. "Considering all we brought to Mars, this is only a handful!"

He started the truck.

Looking at the small white cottage for a long moment, he was filled with a desire to rush to it, touch it, say good-bye to it, for he felt as if he were going away on a long journey, leaving something to which he could never quite return, never understand again.

Just then Sam and his family drove by in another truck.

"Hi, Bittering! Here we go!"

The truck swung down the ancient highway out of town. There were sixty others traveling in the same direction. The town filled with a silent, heavy dust from their passage. The canal waters lay blue in the sun, and a quiet wind moved in the strange trees.

"Good-bye, town!" said Mr. Bittering.

"Good-bye, good-bye," said the family, waving to it.

They did not look back again.

Summer burned the canals dry. Summer moved like flame upon the meadows. In the empty Earth settlement, the painted houses flaked and peeled. Rubber tires upon which children had swung in back yards hung suspended like stopped clock pendulums in the blazing air.

At the metal shop, the rocket frame began to rust.

In the quiet autumn Mr. Bittering stood, very dark now, very golden-eyed, upon the slope above his villa, looking at the valley.

"It's time to go back," said Cora.

"Yes, but we're not going," he said quietly. "There's nothing there any more."

"Your books," she said. "Your fine clothes."

"Your *llles* and your fine *ior uele rre,*" she said.

"The town's empty. No one's going back," he said. "There's no reason to, none at all."

The daughter wove tapestries and the sons played songs on ancient flutes and pipes, their laughter echoing in the marble villa.

Mr. Bittering gazed at the Earth settlement far away in the low valley. "Such odd, such ridiculous houses the Earth people built."

"They didn't know any better," his wife mused. "Such ugly people. I'm glad they've gone."

They both looked at each other, startled by all they had just finished saying. They laughed.

"Where did they go?" he wondered. He glanced at his wife. She was golden and slender as his daughter. She looked at him, and he seemed almost as young as their eldest son.

"I don't know," she said.

"We'll go back to town maybe next year, or the year after, or the year after that," he said, calmly. "Now—I'm warm. How about taking a swim?"

They turned their backs to the valley. Arm in arm they walked silently down a path of clear-running spring water.

Five years later a rocket fell out of the sky. It lay steaming in the valley. Men leaped out of it, shouting.

"We won the war on Earth! We're here to rescue you! Hey!"

But the American-built town of cottages, peach trees, and theaters was silent. They found a flimsy rocket frame rusting in an empty shop.

The rocket men searched the hills. The captain established headquarters in an abandoned bar. His lieutenant came back to report.

"The town's empty, but we found native life in the hills, sir. Dark people. Yellow eyes. Martians. Very friendly. We talked a bit, not much. They learn English fast. I'm sure our relations will be most friendly with them, sir."

"Dark, eh?" mused the captain. "How many?"

"Six, eight hundred, I'd say, living in those marble ruins in the hills, sir. Tall, healthy. Beautiful women."

"Did they tell you what became of the men and women who built this Earth settlement, Lieutenant?"

"They hadn't the foggiest notion of what happened to this town or its people."

"Strange. You think those Martians killed them?"

"They look surprisingly peaceful. Chances are a plague did this town in, sir."

"Perhaps. I suppose this is one of those mysteries we'll never solve. One of those mysteries you read about."

The captain looked at the room, the dusty windows, the blue mountains rising beyond, the canals moving in the light, and he heard the soft wind in the air. He shivered. Then, recovering, he tapped a large fresh map he had thumbtacked to the top of an empty table.

"Lots to be done, Lieutenant." His voice droned on and quietly on as the sun sank behind the blue hills. "New settlements. Mining sites, minerals to be looked for. Bacteriological specimens taken. The work, all the work. And the old records were lost. We'll have a job of remapping to do, renaming the mountains and rivers and such. Calls for a little imagination.

"What do you think of naming those mountains the Lincoln Mountains, this canal the Washington Canal, those hills—we can name those hills for you, Lieutenant. Diplomacy. And you, for a favor, might name a town for me. Polishing the apple. And why not make this the Einstein Valley, and farther over . . . are you *listening,* Lieutenant?"

The lieutenant snapped his gaze from the blue color and the quiet mist of the hills far beyond the town.

"What? Oh, *yes,* sir!"

Glossary

These are names of real people or places mentioned in *Dark They Were, and Golden-Eyed.*

Boston. The capital of Massachusetts, a state on the East Coast of the United States.

Einstein, Albert (1879–1955). German-born scientist. Came up with the theory of relativity, an important new set of ideas in physics.

Ford, Henry (1863–1947). American car maker. Built a big business. Made cars that ordinary people could afford.

Hormel, George A. (1860–1946). American meat packer. Built a big business. Improved conditions for workers.

Idaho. A state in the northwestern United States.

Lincoln, Abraham (1809–1865). Sixteenth president of the United States. In office from 1861 to 1865. Led the nation during the Civil War.

Milwaukee. The largest city in Wisconsin, a state in the midwestern United States.

Minnesota. A state in the midwestern United States.

Ohio. A state in the midwestern United States.

Osseo. The name of different small towns in the midwestern states of Minnesota, Wisconsin and Michigan.

Rockefeller, John D. (1839–1937). American businessman. Made a great deal of money in oil. Famous for his gifts to charities and public works.

Roosevelt, Franklin Delano (1882–1945). Thirty-second president of the United States. In office from 1933 to 1945. Led the nation during the Great Depression and World War II.

Roosevelt, Theodore (1858–1919). Twenty-sixth president of the United States. In office from 1901 to 1909. Protected natural resources. Directed the building of the Panama Canal.

Utah.   A state in the western United States.

Vanderbilt,   Cornelius   (1794–1877). American businessman. Made a large fortune with shipping and railroads.

Washington,   George   (1732–1799). First president of the United States. In office from 1789 to 1797. Led American forces in the War of Independence from England.

Waukegan.   A town in Illinois, a state in the midwestern United States. Ray Bradbury, the author of the story, was born here.

Wisconsin.   A state in the midwestern United States.

Questions for the Reader

THINKING ABOUT THE STORY

1. What was interesting for you about *Dark They Were, and Golden-Eyed?*

2. Were there ways that the events or people in the selection became important or special to you? Write about or discuss these.

3. What do you think were the important things Ray Bradbury wanted to say in the selection?

4. In what ways did the selection answer the questions you had before you began reading or listening?

5. Were any of the parts of the selection difficult to understand? If so, you may want to read or listen to them again. Discuss with your learning partners possible reasons why they were difficult.

THINKING ABOUT THE WRITING

1. How did Ray Bradbury help you see, hear and feel what happened in *Dark They Were, and Golden-Eyed*? Find the words, phrases or sentences that did this best.

2. Writers think carefully about their stories' settings, characters and events. In writing this selection, which of these things do you think Ray Bradbury felt was most important? Find the parts of the story that support your opinion.

3. In *Dark They Were, and Golden-Eyed*, Ray Bradbury creates a feeling of fear, as if something unknown and terrible is going to happen. Go back to the story and find the places where this happens. Think about how Bradbury creates this sense of fear.

4. In the selection, Ray Bradbury talks about things being worn away. Wind, water, chemicals and time all wear away or change the shape of things. Pick out the places where the words suggest that the shapes of things are changing. How do these images, or pictures, support the story that Bradbury is trying to tell?

ACTIVITIES

1. Were there any words that were difficult for you in *Dark They Were, and Golden-Eyed*? Go back to these words and try to figure out their meanings. Discuss what you think each word means, and why you made that guess. Look them up in a dictionary and see if your definition is the same or different.

Discuss with your learning partners how you are going to remember each word. Some ways to remember words are to put them on file cards, or write them in a journal, or create a personal dictionary. Be sure to use the words in your writing in a way that will help you to remember their meaning.

2. Talking with other people about what you have read can increase your understanding. Discussion can help you organize your thoughts, get new ideas and rethink your original ideas. Discuss your thoughts about the selection with someone else who has read it. Find out if you helped yourself understand the selection in the same or in different ways. Find out if your opinions about the selection are the same or different. See if your thoughts change as a result of this discussion.

3. After you finish reading or listening, you might want to write down your thoughts about the book. You could write your reflections on the book in a journal, or you could write about topics the book has brought up that you want to explore further. You could write a book review or a letter to a friend you think might be interested in the book.

4. Did reading the selection give you any ideas for your own writing? You might want to write about:
- a time when you were afraid of the unknown.
- a change that happened while you hardly noticed, such as the change from childhood to adulthood.
- an imagined visit to another planet.

5. Write a description of one of the other planets in the solar system. Jupiter, Saturn and Venus are all good choices. Use books in the library or visit a planetarium. Include the most important facts about the planet you choose. Describe what you see in pictures of the planet.

6. In order to feel at home while he is on

Mars, Harry Bittering surrounds himself with things from Earth. These include flowers, furniture and newspapers. Think about the things you would take to make yourself feel at home in a strange place and make a list or write a description in a journal.

7. If you could talk to Ray Bradbury, what questions would you ask about his writing? You might want to write the questions in a journal.

About Ray Bradbury

Ray Bradbury was born on August 22, 1920, in Waukegan, Illinois. His hometown of Waukegan is mentioned in *Dark They Were, and Golden-Eyed*. It is one of the "Indian prairie" names that Earth people use as names for places on Mars.

As a child, Bradbury loved to read stories and comic strips set in fantastic places. His heroes were the spaceman Flash Gordon and the jungle king Tarzan. He started writing his own stories on a toy typewriter when he was 12.

He wanted to write stories that were entertaining but also made people think. "I write for fun," he later said. "I have fun with ideas."

After graduating from high school, Bradbury was a newsboy in Los Angeles for three years. He sold newspapers by day but at night he wrote stories. "I wrote one or two thousand words a day, year after year," he says. "Most of this I burnt."

Some stories he kept—and sent to magazines. The first story he ever sold appeared in *Super Science Stories* on his twenty-first birthday. Since then, his stories have appeared in many magazines and been collected into books. *Dark They Were, and Golden-Eyed* was originally published in 1949 in the magazine *Thrilling Wonder Stories.* In 1966, it appeared in a book called *S Is for Space.* Bradbury has also written plays, poetry and movie screenplays.

Many of Bradbury's stories are set in the future or in fantastic places. Nearly all of them have a magical, mysterious style.

A student once sent Bradbury a letter asking his secret for success. He answered, "Write every day of your life. . . . To write every day is to know yourself better and to write better and to relax more."

Ray Bradbury lives in Los Angeles, California. He is married and has four daughters.

About Science Fiction and Fantasy

Ray Bradbury has been called "the world's greatest living science fiction writer." But some people say he does not write science fiction at all. Some people say he writes a different kind of story called *fantasy*.

In fantasy, the writer tells about a world that does not exist. What happens in this world may go against known fact. In *The Wizard of Oz*, a fantasy by L. Frank Baum, a tornado picks up a house in the United States and carries it to a kingdom called Oz. But in real life, storms do not carry houses into distant countries. And there is no place called Oz on any map.

A science fiction story is also set in a world that does not exist. But this world is based on scientific fact—on things that *could* happen. In the science fiction novel *2001: A Space Odyssey* by Arthur C. Clarke, a spaceship carries astronauts to the planet Saturn. The spaceship in *2001* is one that could really be built someday. Saturn is described as scientists then knew it to be. The story comes from the writer's imagination but is based on fact.

Most science fiction stories are set in the future. Most involve machines that may someday be invented. Science fiction writers make guesses about the future. Sometimes these guesses come true. Years ago, science fiction writers said there would one day be spaceships, television, computers and atomic bombs. Today these things exist. Other guesses have not yet come true. For example, no one has ever built a time machine.

One of the first science fiction writers was Jules Verne. Verne was a Frenchman who wrote in the 19th century before many of today's machines, such as airplanes, were invented. One of his most famous novels was about a giant submarine that could sink ships. Many years later, real submarines were built that did sink ships in war.

Another science fiction writer from the late 19th century was H. G. Wells. Wells had a good imagination. His novels told about a time machine, an invisible man, a trip to the moon and a war with Mars.

Science fiction magazines began to appear in the 1920s. The magazines printed stories about adventures in space and wars on other planets. Some science fiction writers wrote serious stories about how inventions such as atomic weapons might change people's lives.

Science fiction is still popular today. People watch science fiction movies like *E.T.* and TV shows like *Star Trek.* People read science fiction stories and novels. One writer, Isaac Asimov, author of more than 400 books, has been writing science fiction for over 50 years. Some writers combine fantasy and science fiction in a type of story called *space fantasy.* A space fantasy is set in space but it does not try to stick to scientific facts. The writer puts in anything that will make a good story. The movie *Star Wars* and the comic strip *Flash Gordon* are both space fantasies.

Ray Bradbury's stories about Mars might be called space fantasies instead of science fiction. The way he describes Mars is not at all like the real Mars. But his stories have reality in them. They are about the hopes and fears of ordinary people. They are also beautifully written. That is enough to make a good story—no matter what you call it.

MAP OF THE SOLAR SYSTEM

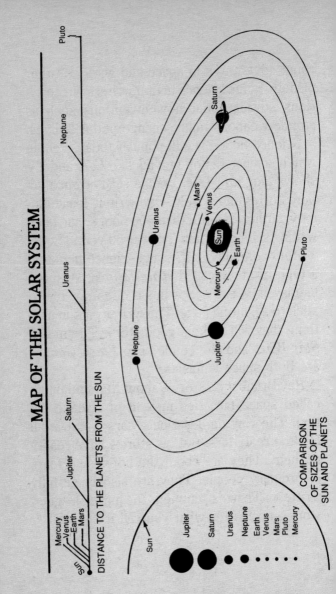

DISTANCE TO THE PLANETS FROM THE SUN

Sun — Mercury — Venus — Earth — Mars — Jupiter — Saturn — Uranus — Neptune — Pluto

COMPARISON OF SIZES OF THE SUN AND PLANETS

Sun — Jupiter — Saturn — Uranus — Neptune — Earth — Venus — Mars — Pluto — Mercury

About Mars

Is there life on Mars? For a long time, people have wondered about this. Writers have written stories about Martian cities and invaders. We now know there is probably no life on Mars. But the real Mars may be even more interesting than the Mars people once imagined.

Mars is one of the nine planets of our solar system. These planets, including Earth, all travel around the sun. See the map of the solar system opposite to find the names of the planets and where they are located.

Mars is the fourth planet away from the sun. It is the second closest planet to Earth. (Our closest neighbor is the planet Venus.) While traveling around the sun, Mars sometimes comes as close as 35 million miles to Earth. At other times it goes farther away. At its farthest, it is 62 million miles away. This is how far a plane would travel if it flew across the United States 24,000 times.

Mars is known as the "red planet." This is because it looks like a red-orange ball. The iron in the soil makes it look red. When iron rusts on Earth, it turns the same color.

Mars is only about half the size of Earth. Its gravity is not as strong as Earth's. This means that things weigh less on Mars. A box of tools that weighed 20 pounds on Earth would weigh less than eight pounds on Mars. A visitor to Mars would jump higher and fall more slowly than on Earth.

Mars is a fascinating planet. In some places, it has rocky plains that look a little like the American Southwest. In other places, there are fields of sand dunes. Other parts are covered by craters like those on our moon.

Mars has big volcanoes. The biggest volcano, Olympus Mons, is 16 miles high. This is almost three times as high as Earth's tallest mountain. Mars also has deep canyons. Many of these canyons are much deeper than the Grand Canyon in the United States.

The north and south poles of Mars look a little like Earth's North and South Poles. They are covered with caps of ice. Some of the ice is frozen water. But some of it is frozen carbon dioxide.

In some parts of Mars, long channels have been cut in the rock. The channels look like riverbeds that have dried up. This is very strange because there is no running water on Mars to cut the channels. Some scientists think that Mars must have had rivers a long time ago. Some scientists believe the water is still frozen underground.

Unlike Earth, which has only one moon, Mars has two. But each of Mars' moons is only a few miles across. Even if they both were put together, they would be much smaller than Earth's moon.

No human being has ever visited Mars. But we have sent unmanned spacecraft to Mars. These machines were controlled by radio from Earth. They took photographs and ran tests. They sent their reports back to Earth through radio and TV waves.

In 1976, two unmanned U.S. spacecraft landed on Mars as part of the Viking program of space exploration. Thanks to Viking and other missions, we now know a great deal about Mars.

The Viking spacecraft found no life on Mars. There are several reasons why Mars probably does not have life as we know it. First, the planet has very little air. Most of the air that Mars has is made of a gas called carbon dioxide. There is almost no oxygen, the gas that most living things on Earth breathe. A person who walked onto Mars without a spacesuit would die at once.

Mars also has no liquid water. There is sometimes ice on Mars but not water that a person could drink. Mars is also cold. It is true that the warmest parts of Mars may reach a comfortable 60 degrees Fahrenheit in daytime in the summer. But at night the same places are as cold as Earth's South Pole. In the winter, temperatures on Mars may fall to 200 degrees below freezing.

Another danger on Mars is radiation from the sun. The sun gives out waves of energy that are harmful to life. On Earth, the air blocks most of these rays. On Mars, there is not enough air to do the same.

Mars also has terrible dust storms. In the summer the winds blow as hard as in the worst hurricanes on Earth. The storms raise dust over large areas. Sometimes clouds of dust cover the entire planet. The sky of Mars is pink because of red dust in the air.

In *Dark They Were, and Golden-Eyed*, Bradbury says a few true things about Mars. For example, he says the winds on the planet are strong. And he says Mars is over 60 million miles from Earth. These things are correct. But Bradbury invents things that are not correct. There are no cities on the real Mars. There is no water to drink or fresh air to breathe.

If people ever live on Mars, they will have to live in a colony that has a heating system and its own supply of air. The colony will need a shield to protect against dangerous rays. The shield can be built of rocks taken from Mars. Plants, animals and supplies can be brought from Earth. This city would not look like the town in *Dark They Were, and Golden-Eyed.* But the people living there would be the first real Martians.

About Space Travel

In *Dark They Were, and Golden-Eyed*, a rocket brings the morning paper from Earth to Mars every day. What would it be like to travel on that rocket?

To go to Mars, a person would have to pass through outer space. Outer space is unlike anything on Earth. To begin with, there is no air in space. The sky is always black. (It is the air on Earth that gives the sky a blue color.) The stars shine much more brightly. Near the sun, space is very hot. Away from the sun, it is very cold. Space is filled with radiation that can be deadly to humans: fast-moving particles called cosmic rays and energy from the sun called ultraviolet light. Both kinds of radiation can be deadly to humans.

Humans cannot live in space unless they carry everything they need—air, water, food—in a spacecraft. The spacecraft must be sealed so that air will not leak out. The walls must be thick to keep out harmful rays. Space travelers must be able to control heat and cold in the spacecraft.

Space begins about 100 miles above the surface of the earth. The only way to get this high is with a rocket. A rocket burns fuel to shoot out gases at high speed. The force of the gases pushes the rocket up into the sky, just as a balloon shoots around when you let out the air. Many space rockets have several stages or sections. When the fuel in one stage is burned up, the stage drops off. Then the rocket uses the fuel in the next stage to keep going faster.

When the spacecraft reaches a certain height and speed, it can enter an orbit around the earth. That means it circles the earth at a regular speed. It is falling *around* the earth without falling back to the earth's surface.

A spacecraft in orbit does not have to burn fuel to keep moving. It keeps moving at the speed it has already reached. That is because there is no air to slow it down.

In orbit, people are weightless. They do not weigh anything because they and the spacecraft are both falling at the same speed. They float instead of walk. Everything floats—food, tools, even drops of water. Nothing stays in its place unless it is tied down.

If a spacecraft goes faster, it can go into an orbit around the sun. Scientists can plan the course of the spacecraft so it goes where they want it. Men have been carried to the moon this way.

Some spacecraft are controlled from Earth by radio and operate without people on board. One spacecraft like this traveled as far as the planet Neptune. It sent back pictures of Neptune and other distant worlds.

In the last few years, space shuttles have flown into orbit around the earth and then returned. The shuttle has wings like a plane. It is carried into space with rockets. When it comes back to Earth, the pilot uses the wings to help the shuttle land.

No human beings have yet landed on Mars. It would take six months to a year to get there, depending on the spacecraft's speed and course. Rockets will probably never go there once a day, as they do in *Dark They Were, and Golden-Eyed*. But someday people may go to Mars.

WRITERS' VOICES

Kareem Abdul-Jabbar and Peter Knobler, *Selected from GIANT STEPS*

Rudolfo A. Anaya, *Selected from BLESS ME, ULTIMA*

Maya Angelou, *Selected from I KNOW WHY THE CAGED BIRD SINGS and THE HEART OF A WOMAN*

Peter Benchley, *Selected from JAWS*

Ray Bradbury, *Selected from DARK THEY WERE, AND GOLDEN-EYED*

Carol Burnett, *Selected from ONE MORE TIME*

Mary Higgins Clark, *Selected from THE LOST ANGEL*

Avery Corman, *Selected from KRAMER vs. KRAMER*

Bill Cosby, *Selected from FATHERHOOD and TIME FLIES*

Louise Erdrich, *Selected from LOVE MEDICINE*

Alex Haley, *Selected from A DIFFERENT KIND OF CHRISTMAS*

Maxine Hong Kingston, *Selected from CHINA MEN and THE WOMAN WARRIOR*

Loretta Lynn with George Vecsey, *Selected from COAL MINER'S DAUGHTER*

Mark Mathabane, *Selected from KAFFIR BOY*

Gloria Naylor, *Selected from THE WOMEN OF BREWSTER PLACE*

Priscilla Beaulieu Presley with Sandra Harmon, *Selected from ELVIS AND ME*

Mario Puzo, *Selected from THE GODFATHER*

Ahmad Rashad with Peter Bodo, *Selected from RASHAD*

Sidney Sheldon, *Selected from WINDMILLS OF THE GODS*

Anne Tyler, *Selected from THE ACCIDENTAL TOURIST*

Abigail Van Buren, *Selected from THE BEST OF DEAR ABBY*

Tom Wolfe, *Selected from THE RIGHT STUFF*

SELECTED FROM CONTEMPORARY AMERICAN PLAYS

SELECTED FROM 20th-CENTURY AMERICAN POETRY

Books are $3.50 each. To order, please send your check to Publishing Program, Literacy Volunteers of New York City, 121 Avenue of the Americas, New York, NY 10013. Please add $2.00 per order and .50 per book to cover postage and handling. NY and NJ residents, add appropriate sales tax. Prices subject to change without notice.